A HOBBY FOR MRS ARBUCKLE

Puffin Books, Penguin Books Australia Ltd
487 Maroondah Highway, PO Box 257, Ringwood, Victoria, 3134, Australia
Penguin Books Ltd, Harmondsworth, Middlesex, England
Viking Penguin Inc., 40 West 23rd Street, New York, NY 10010, USA
Penguin Books Canada Limited, 2801 John Street, Markham, Ontario, Canada, L3R 1B4
Penguin Books (N.Z.) Ltd, 182-190 Wairau Road, Auckland 10, New Zealand

First published in 1989 by Viking Kestrel. Published in Puffin, 1990.

Typeset in Times Bold. Offset from the Viking Kestrel edition.
Made and printed in Hong Kong through Bookbuilders Ltd.

Smyth, Gwenda. A hobby for Mrs Arbuckle.
ISBN 0 14 054152 7.
I. James, Ann. II. Title. (Series: Picture puffins).
A823'.3

A HOBBY FOR MRS ARBUCKLE

Gwenda Smyth and Ann James

Puffin Books

Mrs Emmeline Arbuckle needed a hobby.
She had Mr A. and the gingernut cat
but they didn't fill her life completely.
Mrs Arbuckle told the gingernut cat that she needed a hobby.
'I don't see why,' said the gingernut cat.
'You have a very good pet.'
'Don't try to stop her,' said Mr A.,
'or we'll never hear the end of it.'

'Where do we start?' asked Mrs Arbuckle.
'We must look in the paper for ideas,' said the gingernut cat.
So they borrowed the paper from Mr A.,
but they left him the football pages.

'Aha!' said Mrs Arbuckle. 'I shall be a balloonist
and float across the world.'
She put on her tracksuit and shawl.

They went to a place where a pilot was waiting
with a hot air balloon and a giant basket
and six friends holding it down.
'All aboard!' said the pilot to Mrs Arbuckle,
and 'Stand back!' to the friends.

The balloon ascended very gently.
'Beautiful!' cried Mrs Arbuckle.

The gingernut cat jumped up to see.

'Let go of that rope!' shouted the pilot. 'It lets in cold air.'
Too late. Air rushed in and the balloon went down
faster than it had gone up.
The balloonists rolled out.

The gingernut cat said, 'Just as well you don't have
an elephant for a pet — that's all I can say!'
Mr A. said, 'Find a hobby down on the ground,
for goodness' sake, Emmeline.'

Mrs Arbuckle found an old dustbin and filled it with soil.
'What are you doing now?' asked the gingernut cat.
'Making a worm farm,' replied Mrs Arbuckle,
'and soon I'll be giving worms to every gardener
and fisherperson in the street.'
She put in some fallen leaves, some potato peel
and a rotten apple. Then she added a handful of worms.
'Worms like wetness,' said Mrs Arbuckle,
and she watered the worm farm.
'Worms like darkness,' she said,
and put a sack on top.
'Perfect!' murmured Mrs Arbuckle.

The gingernut cat jumped up on top
to see how the worms were settling in.

The bin tipped over.
There was potato peel all over the pansies,
and the worms all got away.

The gingernut cat said, 'If you fed me
on rotten apples, I'd go away too.'
Mr A. said, 'Emmeline, my dear, why don't you
find a nice indoor hobby?'

Mrs Arbuckle dragged a branch inside
and hung it from the picture rail.
'What are you making today?' asked the gingernut cat.
'The biggest mobile in the world,' said Mrs Arbuckle,
'with pearls and paper birds and pine-cones —'
'— and my best fishing-line,' said Mr A.
He sighed and went to make a custard.

Mrs Arbuckle made twenty-seven paper birds. She threaded
two hundred pearls and painted ninety-nine pine-cones.
'Splendid!' said Mrs Arbuckle.

But the gingernut cat said, 'There's no room to move in here.'

So Mrs Arbuckle hung the mobile from the town hall ceiling.

However, the Lord Mayor wrote her a letter, saying:
Dear Em,
Thank you all the same, but the councillors don't like it.
Pine-cones keep falling on their heads.

'Emmeline,' said Mr A., 'Why don't you find
a nice outdoor hobby?'

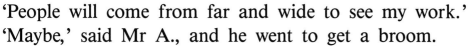

'Why are you sitting on the gatepost?' asked the gingernut cat.
'I'm teaching myself topiary,' said Mrs Arbuckle.
'People will come from far and wide to see my work.'
'Maybe,' said Mr A., and he went to get a broom.

Mrs Arbuckle cut the privet hedge into a row of ducks.
Then she cut the box tree into a rabbit.
'Brilliant!' said Mrs Arbuckle.

She made the cypress tree into a cat, but by mistake
she cut off the cat's ear.
'This is a disgusting hobby,' said the gingernut cat.

Mrs Arbuckle offered to make
the neighbours' yew tree into a rooster.
'Not today, thank you,' said the neighbours.

'I'm afraid I've run out of trees,' said Mrs Arbuckle.
'Good,' replied the gingernut cat, 'because I think trees
should look like trees and not like animals.'
Mr A. swept up the branches. He said, 'Goodness gracious,
Emmeline, why don't you find a plain and simple hobby?'

'What are you making now?' asked the gingernut cat.
'A clown suit,' said Mrs Arbuckle.
'I'm going to learn circus tricks.
And before very long I shall be the talk of the town.'
'Quite likely,' agreed Mr A.,
and he went away to do his jigsaw puzzle.

Mrs Arbuckle went to the circus.
CLOWN CLASS THIS WAY,
said a notice.
Mrs Arbuckle juggled two balls
(but one dropped).
Then she whistled while
she juggled her ball.
'Practice makes perfect,' said the clown
as he helped her on to stilts.
'Thrilling!' cried Mrs Arbuckle.
'Faster!' cried the gingernut cat.

Mrs Arbuckle went down the street, juggling and whistling
and walking on stilts.
'Come down, please Mrs Arbuckle,' said a policeman.
'You are causing a traffic jam.'
'The trouble is,' replied Mrs Arbuckle, 'I can't get down.'
So the policeman brought a crane with a crane-driver,
and Mrs Arbuckle came down to earth.

Mrs Arbuckle and the gingernut cat were home in time
to see themselves on the late-night news.
'Emmeline,' sighed Mr A., 'Can't you think of
a nice, safe hobby?'

Mrs Arbuckle set off with her shopping jeep.
She went to all the second-hand shops in the town.
'What are we looking for?' asked the gingernut cat.
'Hats for my collection,' said Mrs Arbuckle.
'I'm going to have the biggest hat collection in the world,
and every Sunday afternoon people will come
from the ends of the earth to see my hats.'

Mrs Arbuckle found a party hat and a church hat,
a sun hat and a wind hat.
She also found a pith helmet.
She found a bird's nest hat, a fruit salad hat
and a London policeman's hat.
She found a hunter's cap and a lifesaver's cap,
a Dutch bonnet and a Tyrolean dancing hat.

'Look, a tam-o'-shanter!' said Mrs Arbuckle.
She phoned her friends and said, 'I'm collecting hats.'
They brought her a bowler and a boater, a fez and a fedora,
a sombrero and a stetson.
'Magnificent!' cried Mrs Arbuckle.
'And here's a hat for a cat, with two holes for ears.'

Mr A. complained, 'There are hats on my jigsaw
and under my pillow.'
The gingernut cat said, 'There are hats on my cushion and
in my food,' and he went outside and sat in the toolshed.

So Mrs Arbuckle loaded all the hats on her go-cart
and took them to a kindergarten. The children loved them.
Mr A. said, 'Surely to goodness you can find
a useful hobby, Emmeline.'

'What is all this puffing and blowing?' asked the gingernut cat.
'I'm learning the flugelhorn,' said Mrs Arbuckle. 'I'll be able
to call you in for your dinner and signal to ships at sea.'
'Well, not during my football programme,' said Mr A.,
and he went away to do the laundry.

Mrs Arbuckle screwed up her face and blew.
There was no sound.
She blew in several different ways.
'Try the other end,' said the gingernut cat.

There was a long, loud note.
'Glorious!' gasped Mrs Arbuckle,
and she did it again and again.

But the neighbours came to the door and said,
'Please, Mrs Arbuckle! Our baby is hiding under the bed,
our dog has gone under the house,
and they won't come out until you stop!'

Mr A. gave the flugelhorn back to the city band.
He said, 'Please find a quiet hobby, Emmeline.'

'I wonder why you are digging up the lawn,'
said the gingernut cat.
'I'm going to be a pole-vaulter,' said Mrs Arbuckle.
'I'll probably win a medal in the next Olympic Games.'
'Well, don't land in the lettuces,' said Mr A.,
and he went away to darn his socks.

Mrs Arbuckle dug a sandpit.
She made a bamboo pole and put up
a bar.

Mrs Arbuckle ran as fast as she could. She planted the pole and up she went. Her legs pointed to the sky.
'Unreal!' shouted Mrs Arbuckle.

The gingernut cat jumped up on the bar to watch.

Down came the bar and the gingernut cat.
Down came Mrs Arbuckle in the rhubarb.

'Some things are not as easy as they look,'
said the gingernut cat, 'even for cats.'
Mr A. said, 'Get a ladylike hobby,
for pity's sake, Emmeline.'

Mrs Arbuckle put on her boilersuit and her rubber boots.
'Where on earth are you going?' asked the gingernut cat.
'I'm going caving,' said Mrs Arbuckle. 'I'll probably find
a secret cave that has never been found before.'
Mr A. said, 'I don't think you're built for it, Emmeline.'
'*I'm* built for it,' said the gingernut cat.

They went to a hole in a cliff where a leader was waiting
with a long, thin ladder and a long, thin rope
and two long, thin cave-explorers.
They gave Mrs Arbuckle a helmet with a light on it.
They put a rope around her middle.
'Down we go!' said the leader.

The cave was dark, with stalactites
and stalagmites and crystal helictites.
'Fabulous!' whispered Mrs Arbuckle.

They came to a narrow tunnel.
The leader went through. The gingernut cat went through.
Mrs Arbuckle stuck halfway.

The cave explorers pulled her out.
Mrs Arbuckle and the gingernut cat went up the ladder.

They were home before dark.
'That's a hobby for rabbits,' said the gingernut cat,
'if you want my opinion.'
Mr A. said, 'Never mind. I'll make a cup of tea.'

Mrs Arbuckle was sad. She said, 'All my hobbies go wrong.'
The gingernut cat said, 'You need a hobby which is
not messy or difficult and not dangerous or noisy.
You need a hobby that is neither up in the air
nor down in the ground, and which won't upset the neighbours.
That's the kind of hobby you need.'

Mrs Arbuckle sat down to ponder.

There was a lot of knocking on the door.
'Emmeline,' said Mr A., 'there's a balloonist at the door
who needs some glue to mend his basket...
and a cave explorer who wants her helmet back.
There's a Lord Mayor with a giant mobile...
and a neighbour who wants her hedge shaped like a teapot.
There's a musician to teach you the trombone...
a girl who needs a dozen worms...
and a Guardsman with a busby.
There's a clown to give you a juggling lesson...
and a boy who wants to play in the sandpit.'

'Not just now,' said Mrs Arbuckle.
'I'm learning the art of relaxation,'
and she lay down on the floor.
'What shall I do with the visitors?' asked Mr A.
There was no reply.
Mrs Arbuckle was fast asleep.